Dear Grace
Elizabeth
May God Bless
you as you walk/grow
faithfully with Him.

Blessings

Louise &
Emily Anderson

In memory of your
Mom's friend

Jamie.

Sweet Beginnings from the Bible

BABY STORIES GOD TOLD

DAVID & HEATHER KOPP

HARVEST HOUSE PUBLISHERS
EUGENE, OREGON

Dedication

For Jim and Tami Lloyd, and their seven precious baby stories:
Isaac, Jael, Eve, Grace, Esther, Josiah, and Chloe

Baby Stories God Told

Copyright © 1999 by David and Heather Kopp
Published by Harvest House Publishers
Eugene, Oregon 97402

Library of Congress Cataloging-in-Publication Data
Kopp, David, 1949—
    Baby stories God told / David and Heather Kopp.
        p.   cm.
    ISBN: 1-56507-822-5
    1. Infants in the Bible.   2. Bible stories, English.   I. Kopp,
Heather Harpham, 1964—   II. Title.
BS576.K66   1999
242'.5—dc21   98-38536
                                                              CIP

Design and Production by Koechel Peterson & Associates, Minneapolis, Minnesota

Printed in the United States of America.

99 00 01 02 03 04 05 06 07 08 / BG / 10 9 8 7 6 5 4 3 2 1

Babies on His Mind

"Every baby comes as evidence that God still dreams of Eden."
—Calvin Miller

Have you ever noticed how much God loves to tell stories? As you read along in the Bible, you meet great kings, march off to war, endure flood and plague and heartbreak. But if you listen very carefully in the clamor of Jewish history-in-the-making, you'll hear another sound. A gurgling, cooing sound. Because the Creator of the universe loves baby stories, too.

In an earlier book titled *Love Stories God Told*, we explored romantic love in the Bible. As you might expect, these stories usually didn't end with attraction or even marriage. Right after God tells us about first looks and pounding hearts, He unfolds inspiring stories of pregnancy, childbirth, and babies.

In fact, babies were God's only new creation after the Fall. With Eve's pregnancy, God seemed to be declaring, "Be full of hope! Be blessed with joy!" And one day, when God wanted to bring eternal life back to His fallen planet, He appeared to a young couple named Mary and Joseph. He had a baby story to tell—of His very own Son, soon to be born.

You'll notice that most of the Bible's baby stories are about the births of boys. This is because ancient cultures placed a high value on sons (they carried on the family name and provided financial security). Yet in each delightful account it is the women—mothers—who take center stage and shine.

We can all relate to Rebekah, enormously pregnant with active twins, when she groans, "Will my delivery day ever come?!" We laugh along with Sarah, because every birth is a miracle and cause for joy. With Ruth, we realize again how important one baby can be to the entire extended family. And with Hannah, we understand not only the joy of answered prayer, but the bittersweet surrender of letting go to God what we cherish most.

As you read these retellings from the Bible, and gaze into the face of your own precious baby, may you see a miracle you might have missed. Another baby story God can't wait to tell.

Table of Contents

1. Then God Made Baby   p. 7
   THE FIRST MOTHER GIVES BIRTH

2. Promise of Laughter   p. 13
   THE BIRTH OF BABY ISAAC

3. A Baby Like No Other   p. 20
   THE BIRTHS OF BABIES JACOB AND ESAU

4. A Longing Fulfilled   p. 27
   THE BIRTHS OF THE 12 SONS OF ISRAEL

5. Safe in God's Care   p. 35
   THE BIRTH OF BABY MOSES

6. *Help from Heaven*   p. 42
THE BIRTH OF BABY SAMSON

7. *Grandma's Pride and Joy*   p. 49
THE BIRTH OF BABY OBED

8. *A Mother's Gift*   p. 56
THE BIRTH OF BABY SAMUEL

9. *In the Secret Place*   p. 64
THE BIRTH OF JOHN THE BAPTIST

10. *God's Own Baby*   p. 71
THE BIRTH OF BABY JESUS

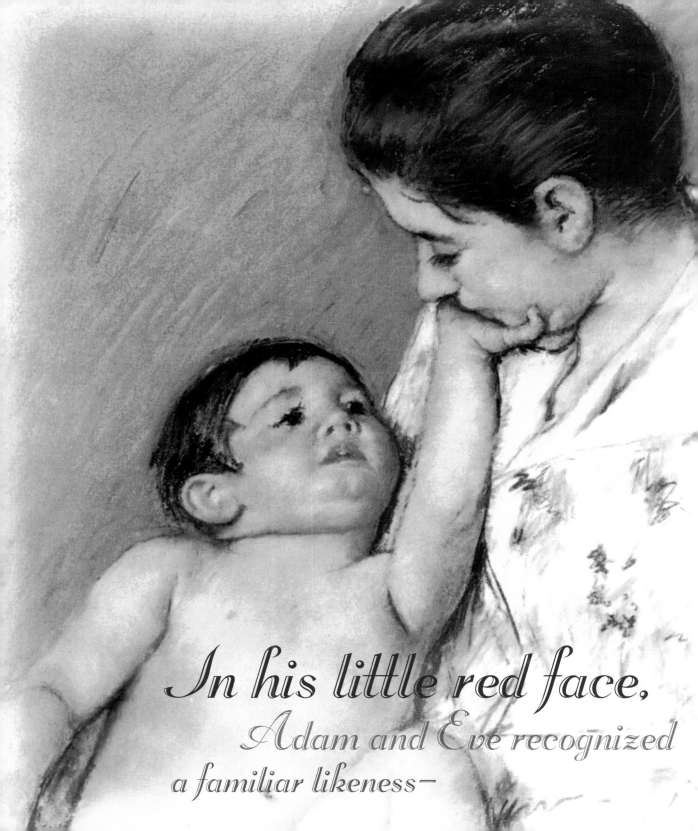

In his little red face,
Adam and Eve recognized
a familiar likeness—

Then God Made Baby

The First Mother Gives Birth

The First Mother Gives Birth

For you created my inmost being; you knit me together in my mother's womb.

Psalm 139:13

One night when they were eating their simple meal together, Eve suddenly spoke up. "Adam, today, while I was doing nothing in particular, I felt…a twinge, a surging inside me…"

"Uh-huh," Adam mumbled. "Did you eat some kumquats that weren't ripe yet?"

"I don't think so," said Eve thoughtfully.

A week later, Eve and her husband were pulling weeds from their garden before the sun got too hot. "Adam," said Eve, "this morning I'm not feeling well. There's a struggle in my stomach, a wretched queasiness…"

"Why don't you lie down in the shade?" Adam suggested.

"I'll be fine," Eve said with a sigh. And as the day wore on, her misery seemed to pass.

But within a few weeks, Eve had a new complaint, one she found herself repeating more and more often. "Adam, I'm getting so fat!"

Adam had to agree. He laughed and touched her smooth, rounding belly. "I like it!" he declared.

"Adam," Eve ventured in a quiet voice. "Do you think I am like the does on the meadow…the ones who are carrying their young?"

Her husband looked startled. "Are you…?"

"Oh, Adam!" cried Eve. "I've been suspecting it for some time now. I think I am carrying a baby!"

Adam looked shocked. He could only smile and sputter, "You're…you're…?"

"Oh, Adam! I think I am carrying a baby!"

"Often, I feel so happy about it," Eve went on excitedly. "But I worry, too. Didn't the Lord say I would have great pain with my babies? So is this…more punishment?"

"Surely, nothing good has been created since we had to leave Eden," Adam agreed, taking Eve into his arms. "But you've seen the fawns, my love. They are beautiful, and they stay close to the doe who bore them. It might be a wonderful thing to make another one of…us!"

After that, Adam enjoyed lying beside Eve in the shade of a tree and stroking her abdomen. Day by day her tummy swelled until it was as large and firm as a melon. "God made me from dirt…" Adam muttered one day while Eve napped beside him. "He made her from my rib. What is the woman's child made from?"

Swiftly the weeks passed. Adam sweated in the sun against weeds and thorns. But Eve rested more, increasingly aware of the new life forming within her body. And still she grew! How long until the baby came? And how would a being this large, they both wondered, ever emerge from *her?*

Every day, Eve observed the animals closely.

8

"Adam," she said one night while they lay down to sleep together, "after I give birth, the baby and I will both help you in the garden. It takes the newborn fawns a few hours to stand and walk. But a human should learn quicker than a deer, don't you think?"

Her husband smiled. "Yes, Eve. And what do you think our baby will say to us? If we can speak, surely, our baby will speak!"

The very next morning, as the sun was just coming over the horizon, the pain of labor came upon Eve. She cried out in distress for many hours. And with every contraction, the Lord's words rang in her ears like a terrible fate. *With pain you will give birth to children.*

Adam sat near her side, amazed at what Eve, *his* help-meet, could do. Powerful instincts—strength, concentration, and courage—seemed to rise up from somewhere inside of her. And he, ruler over every creature, could only wring his hands and mutter lame comforts....

Baby's Breath
WAITING

Dear Baby,
Here beneath my heart,
I thought that you
might come today;
the timing just seemed right.

But the stars are out
and the moon is high
and sheepishly I wonder why
I try to arrange the plans of God.

For now I know
you will not come
until the One who holds eternity
rustles your soft cocoon and
whispers in tones
that I will not hear,
"It's time, precious gift.
Now it's time."

—Robin Jones Gunn

9

Baby in Bible Times

CRIES OF PAIN, TEARS OF JOY

Some things about having a baby haven't changed since Bible times at all. From the first time Eve gave birth, and the earth heard "a cry as of a woman in labor, a groan as of one bearing her first child" (Jeremiah 4:31), having a baby has hurt.

God warned Eve that she would have great pain in childbirth. But Genesis doesn't mention the rest of the story—joy! Ask any woman who's given birth to a baby what it was like, and she'll probably reply, "Oh, it was terrible! I've never been in so much pain…Of course, it was the most wonderful experience of my life!"

How familar! Distress followed by elation and wonder.

In fact, every woman can take heart in remembering that a woman's pain in childbirth is only a prelude to one of the greatest joys she will experience. Jesus himself put it this way,

"A woman giving birth to a child has pain because her time has come; but when her baby is born she forgets the anguish because of her joy that a child is born into the world" (John 16:21).

10

While a son was born.

Adam wordlessly lifted up the tiny, slippery, wrinkled baby human being. The first in the universe. Eve could hardly grasp the mystery of it. From woman, taken from man, had come a man-child. *"With the Lord's help, I have brought forth a man!"* she declared.

And yet, the baby was so helpless! He was nothing like they had imagined…but he was surely nothing less. In his little red face, Adam and Eve recognized a familiar likeness— the image of themselves and their Maker.

Adam leaned down and kissed Eve's damp forehead as he gently handed her the small being. "God's creation miracles did not end in Eden, did they?" he whispered.

Eve met Adam's eyes. She smiled and held their baby to her breast. And as the baby quietly nursed, the world's first mother began to understand the wonder of her name—Eve, "the life-giving one."

"With the Lord's help, I have brought forth a man!"

I praise you for the miracle

The Miracle of Motherhood

Lord,

Thank you for the great
privilege of being a woman.

I praise you for the miracle
of pregnancy and birth.

What an amazing, marvelous idea!
Please bless the little life I bring
into the world and help me always
to be aware of the miracle
you have entrusted to me…

Draw close to my child
as she wakes and as she sleeps.

Grant her the innocence of Eden
and the hope of redemption.

And give me the courage and beauty
of Eve, the first woman to know the
amazing miracle of motherhood.

Amen

12

Promise of Laughter

The Birth of Baby Isaac

May your father and mother be glad; may she who gave you birth rejoice!
Proverbs 23:25

Sarah had always been a beautiful woman. "Jewel of the Morning," her husband Abraham had called her. Even now, when she wore an old woman's shawls, he insisted she was stunning and desirable.

But Sarah knew differently. After all, she was 90. She saw the lines in her face— anyone could.

Abraham had never given up his lifelong conviction that God was going to give them many descendants. But decades had passed, and with them opportunities. Her womb had long ago dried up, leaving her old and childless. Could even God change that?

Until only days ago, she had simply stopped asking…

Then last week, her husband had arrived home from a long walk with an expression of awe on his face. "God made a covenant with me," he told her breathlessly. "He is going to make my descendants into a great nation, his chosen people. And you, Sarah, will give birth to the son from whom this nation will come!"

At first, Sarah hadn't known what to think. She was sure that her husband listened to God. And that God would make a covenant with him didn't surprise her. "But when—and *how*—is this supposed to happen?" she asked Abraham, shaking her head.

"And you, Sarah, will give birth to the son from whom this nation will come!"

14

"God said you will bear a son a year from now."

Since hearing those startling words, Sarah had pondered them almost every waking moment. She wished she'd heard God speak herself. What was Abraham—or God—thinking of? How on earth could a woman her age get pregnant? Such a thing was unheard of.

Now it was the heat of the day as she mulled these thoughts over, and so she wasn't particularly happy when Abraham burst into the tent with orders. "Quick!" he shouted. "We've got visitors. Prepare some food."

While a servant scurried to get some meat ready, Sarah worked on the bread—but not before she peeked out the tent opening to see who had arrived. Three men. But these were no ordinary men—they appeared to be angels!

If only women were welcome among the circles of men as they talked, she thought. And then Sarah realized that the visitors were close enough for her to overhear. Quietly, she moved toward the front of the tent. And that's when she heard one of them say, "Where is your wife, Sarah?"

"She's in the tent," said Abraham.

Sarah froze. Was she supposed to be hearing this? Then one of the visitors spoke. "I will surely return to you about this time next year, and Sarah your wife will have a son."

This time, Sarah had heard the incredible news with her own ears. She gasped. *Was she, wrinkled as a dried fig and worn out as well, really to bear a child?* Before she could stop herself, she laughed out loud.

A few minutes later, Abraham burst back into the tent. "Why did you laugh?" he asked her. "They heard you laugh. And then they said, 'Is anything too hard for the Lord?'"

Sarah was speechless. Had she laughed with disbelief? With bitterness? With hope? She wasn't sure—and she could see Abraham was upset.

"I didn't really laugh," she finally said, trying to sound sincere.

"Yes, you did," her husband insisted. "You laughed."

That was the end of the matter for some time, but Sarah slept with Abraham as often as possible. And she waited and watched, and waited and watched, and every time she laughed, one thought filled her heart, *Baby!*

15

Baby in Bible Times
EVERY CHILD IS A PROMISE

During Bible times, Baby's birth was as much a special event as it is today. Certain people were expected to be present, and special procedures were carefully carried out.

Maid-servants—and whenever possible, midwives—helped during a childbirth. After the umbilical cord was cut, Baby was washed, then rubbed with salts and oils to protect Baby's skin. Then Baby was wrapped tightly in strips of linen—the "swaddling clothes" of the Christmas story—for protection.

Boys were circumcised with a flint knife at eight days as a reminder of the promise that every descendant of Abraham (male and female) was one of God's chosen people and would receive his blessing.

Though some procedures of Baby's arrival have changed, how wonderful to know that the occasion still comes complete with God's promise:

"I will establish my covenant as an everlasting covenant between me and you and your descendants...to be your God" (Genesis 17:7).

Three months passed. And then, just as God had promised, Sarah became pregnant. The wrinkles had lied. The impossible had happened.

Now Sarah put away her shawls and proudly wore the garment of a young expectant wife. Her body seemed to grow younger and more lovely every day. With every change, old doubts subsided, and her spirit seemed to sigh and stretch, like a parched flower receiving rain.

When Sarah's hour to deliver finally arrived, the words of the angel came back in a chant to carry her through the pain of childbirth:

Nothing is too hard for the Lord!

Nothing is too hard for the Lord!

Abraham was all smiles when he named his new son. "This boy will be called…Isaac," he announced. Isaac means "laughter."

That evening, Sarah reached down and held her baby's tiny fingers in her own—so small! And his little wrinkled face, especially when he was about to cry, looked even older than her own.

Is anything too hard for you, Lord? she whispered.

"God has brought me laughter," she told her husband. "And everyone who hears about this will laugh with me."

Sarah laughed then, and so did Abraham. But this time, she knew her laugh was one of purest joy. And she was certain she would never again doubt that God would do anything that he promised.

Baby's Breath
INFANT JOY

I have no name:
'I am but two days old.'
What shall I call thee?
'I happy am,
Joy is my name.'
Sweet joy befall thee!

Pretty joy!
Sweet joy but two days old,
Sweet joy I call thee:
Thou dost smile,
I sing the while,
Sweet joy befall thee!

—William Blake

17

A Baby Is God's Laughter

Heavenly Father,

Nothing is too hard for you!
In the least-promising situations
you do what you say you will do.
When you want to do something
extraordinary, you begin with nothing
but the faith of ordinary people.
Hear my laughter today!
And may the sound echo
down through the years
like baby Isaac's first cooing sighs.
May I never forget to rejoice
when I think about the miracle
of life you have given me.
You are worthy of my happy praise,
for you always do what you say you will do.
You keep every single promise.
And each day, if I ask, you will help me
grow in faith and trust in you.

Amen

Hear my laughter today!

18

"God has brought me laughter."

A Baby Like No Other

The Births of Babies Jacob and Esau

*I praise you because I am fearfully and wonderfully made;
your works are wonderful, I know that full well.*

Psalm 139:14

Rebekah had known she would love Isaac since the first moment she'd seen him coming across a field toward her. Here was a man with a future—"the son of promise," her father had called Isaac when the marriage was being arranged.

Leaving family and friends a thousand miles away for such a man seemed like the adventure of a lifetime. And a smart choice. Together she and Isaac would seek and grasp God's best…

In fact, as soon as they'd married, Rebekah had begun to dream of the babies she'd give Isaac. Pink, plump, smooth-skinned babies with Isaac's nose. She could just picture them!

But years passed— 20 heartbreaking years of trying to conceive— and Rebekah still had no children. How could her husband be the "father of many generations," as Grandpa Abraham always promised, when the couple couldn't even have *one* baby? Nothing was going according to plan.

Finally, after a special time of prayer for her by her husband, Rebekah became pregnant.

Very pregnant!

By only her fifth month, she lay prostrate in her tent during the heat of the day, sure that if she put on any more weight, she would be mistaken for a hippopotamus. "Oh, you're going to have a *big* one, Rebekah!" her friends teased.

And Rebekah's middle kept getting larger. But size was only part of the ordeal. The other was all the commotion in her tummy. The baby seemed to have a dozen extra elbows and knees—and the determination to push with all of them, all at once.

"Is it supposed to feel this way—like a war that never stops?" she asked Deborah, the family nurse.

"That's just the baby kicking," Deborah reassured her.

"I think he's going to be a very strong baby," Isaac said proudly.

But one day, as Rebekah's girth kept right on swelling, the commotion inside brought her to the end of her patience.

"Is this turmoil what I've waited for all these years?" she finally exclaimed, holding her taut belly. "I can't endure this!"

That night, Rebekah prayed. "You brought me all this way to marry Isaac, Lord. Have you forgotten me?" she asked. "Why is having the baby you've promised so hard? And why this terrible struggle in my womb?"

21

Rebekah knew she was giving Isaac not one baby with his nose, but two.

And God answered her: *"Two nations are in your womb…one will be stronger than the other, and the older will serve the younger"* (Genesis 25:23).

Two nations? So she was pregnant with not just one child, but twins. No wonder!

She rushed to tell Isaac and Deborah and anyone who would listen. "Can you believe it?" Rebekah whooped. "A double blessing! Two nations!"

"Well, at least that explains the wrestling match in there!" Isaac said.

The rest of Rebekah's pregnancy was at least tolerable. She knew she was giving Isaac not one baby with his nose, but two.

Through the rest of the hot season, Rebekah rested, sipped medicinal teas, and cooled her brow with splashes of mintwater. *At least when they're born, I'll have a little more peace,* she thought.

But when birthing day finally arrived, Rebekah's hope that "things would feel right again" quickly faded. More surprises were in store.

The first to come out was red, and his whole body was like a hairy garment; so they named him Esau [meaning "hairy"]. After this, his brother came out, with his hand grasping Esau's heel; so he was named Jacob [meaning "grabber"] (Genesis 25:25).

22

Everyone said that Rebekah's twins must have come from God because it sure didn't look like they came from Isaac and Rebekah! And how different they were even from each other. Baby Jacob was watchful and frail, but Baby Esau was loud, strong, and always ravenous.

And neither one of them had Isaac's nose.

Rebekah loved both her babies. She was never happier than when she was in her tent, nursing first one son, then the other, cooing the lullabies she had learned as a girl. *I'm singing to my double blessing,* she thought. *I'm cradling two nations at my breast.*

As the little boys grew, Rebekah often felt disappointment that they didn't play together like other brothers. Instead, Jacob and Esau quarrelled and fussed over everything. *Can God's promises for our family still come true?* Rebekah wondered. Everything kept turning out harder than she had imagined.

Baby's Breath
LOST IN WONDER

Two dimpled hands,
Ten tiny toes,
One rosebud mouth,
One snubby nose.
A pair of bright eyes,
Twin pools of blue,
Sunshine and showers
Reflecting through.
A soft gurgling laugh,
An innocent smile,
A good healthy yell
Once in a while.

I'm lost in the wonder
Of life's greatest joy
As I gaze on the face
Of my wee sleeping boy.

—Milly Walton

23

Baby in Bible Times

I HAVE CALLED YOU BY NAME

Can you imagine naming your baby "Hairy" or "Grabber"?

It was common in Bible times to name Baby after something that described the baby's features, Mommy's feelings, or events surrounding the birth. Trying to win her husband's affections by giving him sons, Jacob's wife, Leah ("wild cow") named her oldest son Reuben ("See, a son!").

We still choose Baby's name for very personal reasons. After all, a name says, "You're special, you're mine—and I love you!" Only today, we're more likely to choose a name for how it sounds or who it's associated with, or because we want to honor a family member or friend.

No matter what we name our baby, he or she ultimately belongs to God and is intimately known by him. As the prophet Isaiah declared, *"This is what the LORD says,…O Israel: 'Fear not, for I have summoned you by name; you are mine'"* (Isaiah 43:1).

24

But sometimes in the years to come, as the sounds of boys playing—and arguing and fighting—echoed across the fields, Rebekah would lie in her tent and think about what strong young men they were becoming. At least their constant challenges were sharpening every skill and character trait.

Of course! she thought, *with a double blessing comes a double challenge. God had never promised that her great adventure with Isaac would be easy.*

In fact, surely God had created the startling differences in her boys on purpose. Maybe, she decided, he needed two brothers striving *against* each other to raise up one "son of promise" strong enough for the future he had planned…

I'm cradling
two nations
at my breast.

May I celebrate each child

My Baby Is Amazing

Lord,

Thank you that you have a special
destiny in store for every mother
and for every baby born,
and that your timing is always perfect,
even when it seems slow—
or too fast to me.

I pray that each of the babies I bear
gets loved as equally as possible
by their daddy and their mommy.

Thank you that each of them will be
unique and special, whether boy
or girl, loose blond curls or tight black
twirls, whether outgoing or shy,
whether fast or slow, chubby or tiny.

Help me to teach all my children
to love you, and to love each other!

May I celebrate each child and help
bring about your plans for them
by creating a home of peace
and harmony.

Amen

A Longing Fulfilled

I will pour out my spirit on your offspring, my blessing on your descendants.
Isaiah 44:3

Were there ever two sisters more at odds? Was ever one sister's happiness so much another sister's grief?

Rachel often asked herself such questions while she watched her sister, Leah, calm and tall, nursing her babies or cooing quietly while she patted their tiny, smooth backs. Leah was every husband's dream wife—she made boy babies. Leah had sons outside playing, a son to pass around to relatives, a son to nurse...

But Rachel—small-boned, intense, and pretty—had none.

Rachel spent a great deal of time helping her sister take care of their growing family.

And when Leah wasn't looking, Rachel would often pick up a handsome nephew, cuddle him close, and wonder sadly why God had not granted her babies of her own.

Girl babies, boy babies—O Lord, how I'd love a baby of my own! she would sigh.

Then she would thank God that Jacob, her devoted husband, still loved her—babies or no. All their friends and family agreed it was a shame that she bore him no children. After all, everyone knew it was Rachel whom Jacob had truly loved from the start. It was Rachel he'd worked 14 years to marry.

Yet by a heartless trick of her father, it was her sister who'd married Jacob first.

27

"I want to give you a son— and hold a baby that is mine..."

And now Leah had already given Jacob four sons. Some people said God was blessing Leah with babies because he had blessed Rachel with Jacob's love. But as the years passed, Rachel thought more and more that she'd gladly trade at least *some* of Jacob's affection for the chance to hold a baby of her own.

One evening, when Jacob came home from the fields, Rachel met him at the door. Tears streamed down her face.

"What is it, Rachel? What's wrong?"

"What's wrong? What's always wrong!" she sobbed. "If you don't give me a baby I'll die!"

Jacob bristled. "I sleep with you as often as possible as it is, Rachel. I can't neglect my other wife, you know. If you want a baby, go ask God! I am not God. Haven't you noticed?"

Her husband's rebuke stung. But Rachel knew that he was right. The problem was hers, not his. And she'd have to solve it herself.

That night, she decided on a plan. She announced to Jacob that she wanted him to sleep with her servant, Bilhah. "It's my right to ask this," she said, "because of how much I want to give you a son— and hold a baby that is mine, not Leah's!"

Jacob agreed, and soon Bilhah became pregnant and delivered a boy, which Rachel adopted as her own. "God has vindicated me," she exclaimed to all who would listen. "He has listened to my plea and given me a son."

Before Leah could get pregnant, Bilhah bore Jacob a second son. Now six rambunctious boys filled Jacob's house—and two of them belonged, at least by custom, to Rachel. She told everyone, "I have had a great struggle with my sister, and I have won!"

But sometimes as Rachel lay awake at night next to Jacob, she thought about what she and her sister were really trying to win. She wanted a child, of course, but what Leah wanted most was her husband's love. Rachel had seen the hopeful look in her sister's eyes every time she had born Jacob another son. Maybe now Jacob would favor her. After all, she was bringing him honor and making him rich with heirs.

Yet Rachel knew that neither wife was any closer to winning. She was still barren. And Leah was still overlooked…

Not that Leah quit trying. When her pregnancies suddenly stopped, she too offered her maid to Jacob. And soon Leah's brood of sons by Jacob had swelled by another two.

Baby's Breath
SLEEP, BABY, SLEEP

Sleep, baby, sleep,
Thy father guards the sheep;
Thy mother shakes
the dreamland tree
And from it fall sweet
dreams for thee,
Sleep, baby, sleep.

—Lavender's Blue,
   Nursery Rhymes

29

Baby in Bible Times

THE GRACE OF BABIES

In Bible times, having children meant a great deal to a couple's future—your wealth would grow, you would be cared for in old age, and the family name would endure. When Jacob left home, his father Isaac gave him a traditional blessing: *"May God Almighty bless you and make you fruitful and increase your numbers"* (Genesis 28:3).

Because the ability to bear children was such a source of pride for Hebrew women, a wife who couldn't conceive often experienced deep shame. Barrenness was believed to be a sure sign of God's displeasure. No wonder when Rachel finally bore Joseph, she declared, *"God has taken away my disgrace"* (Genesis 30:23).

When a wife was unable to have babies or stopped having them, sometimes a maidservant gave birth for her. At the delivery, the wife would receive the child onto her knees, a sign that Baby was legally adopted into the family—and equally received by God.

In the case of Rachel, Leah, and their maidservants, God used all four mothers to accomplish his purposes. He was, after all, at work on an ambitious plan—to give Jacob 12 sons, who would someday become the 12 tribes of the nation Israel.

One day, when boys seemed everywhere underfoot, Leah's oldest son Reuben brought some mandrake roots to his mother. She was thrilled to have them, since everyone believed that mandrakes could help a woman become more fertile. Perhaps Leah would start bearing children again.

Rachel was alarmed. "Can I have some of your son's mandrakes?" she asked.

She hardly expected Leah to say yes. But she didn't expect the fire in Leah's usually placid eyes. "Wasn't it enough that you took away my husband?" she screeched. "Now you want my son's mandrakes, too?"

Rachel could hardly believe her ears. *Who took whose husband away? Hadn't her sister stolen her husband on their wedding night, pretending to be Rachel?*

"Fine," Rachel finally answered. "You can have Jacob tonight, in return for the mandrakes."

That evening, Rachel watched Leah go out to meet Jacob as he returned from the fields. With a sudden stab, Rachel wondered if she'd made the right choice. But what harm could one night do? Especially when she had the mandrakes?

She watched Leah returning to the house, and one of her children running out to meet her and Jacob. Leah. Leah who used to whisper with her in the night. Leah, who used to be so kind…Rachel missed having a sister, but not as much as she missed having her own baby.

Rachel soon realized that the mandrakes had failed to make her fertile. And a short while later, Leah gave Jacob a fifth son, and the next year, a sixth. Now Jacob was the proud father of 10 sons—and Rachel was still barren.

Rachel gave up hope. She would never be able to compete with her sister, the dream wife. No husband's love, no mysterious roots, no scheming could make Rachel a mother.

And then the unimaginable happened. Rachel seemed to be…no, she certainly was…*pregnant!* Could it be that her heart's desire was about to be fulfilled? And now, after she had finally resigned herself to a lonely fate? Rachel wept in Jacob's arms with joy and anticipation.

Every day of her growing pregnancy seemed to Rachel like a gift, a grace, a vindication. And one day she delivered into Jacob's arms a beautiful son. She named him Joseph. At every opportunity, she told her family, "God remembered me, and with this boy he has taken away my disgrace."

Every day of her growing pregnancy seemed to Rachel like a gift, a grace...

32

Immediately, Rachel asked God for another son. But it was some years later before she conceived again. Then, in the process of giving birth to Baby Benjamin—the last baby ever born to Jacob—Rachel died…

Growing up as the youngest brother of 12 famous sons—whose descendants became the 12 tribes of Israel—Benjamin often heard his family's amazing story. How his mother and aunt fiercely competed for the privilege of having sons. How thrilled Rachel had been to discover she was pregnant a second time. And how, in the end, God used the tricks of a father-in-law and the rivalry of two sisters to build a chosen nation.

Could it be
that her heart's desire
was about to be fulfilled?

34

A Mother's Longing

Lord,

You gave mothers the sweet desire
to have babies, to hold them close
and raise them with love.

How urgently we feel this desire, O God!

And yet, though we scheme and plot and plan,
we are not the ones who make it happen.

You are the Giver of life.

You perform your miracles of conception,
pregnancy and perfectly growing unborn
child—while a mother watches wonderstruck!

How I praise you!

Bless my mother-heart, O Lord.

Just as you blessed the striving
and heartache of Rachel and Leah,
use my human longings—weaknesses
and all—to unfold another of your amazing
miracles in my world, and bring glory
to your name.

Amen

Bless my mother-heart

Safe in God's Care

THE BIRTH OF BABY MOSES

The eternal God is your refuge, and underneath are the everlasting arms.
Deuteronomy 33:27

When the slave mother saw that she had delivered a boy, her heart sank. These were the worst of times for boy babies. Why couldn't her new baby have been a girl?

Surely, here was a baby with no future. Pharaoh, King of Egypt, had declared that all Hebrew boys must be killed at birth. These Hebrew immigrants were overrunning his kingdom, his advisers had said. What if they ever decided to rebel?

"If you see a Hebrew baby boy, throw it in the Nile!" Pharaoh had told the midwives.

And now, the Jewish slave mother saw that her baby was not only beautiful, but there was something more…something in his face that made this birth even more bittersweet. The midwife bending to look at the baby's face saw it too. "Surely, this boy was meant for something great!" she declared with heavy sighs.

What was the mother to do?

She decided to simply hide him as long as possible. Her two older children, Miriam and Aaron, would have to help with the conspiracy. There'd be no announcements, no new-baby parties, no showing off her handsome son to the other women on market day. She'd go right back to work in the sweltering fields with the other slaves. If anyone asked, her family would pretend that the pregnancy had ended tragically, with a private burial.

Baby in Bible Times
ADOPTED INTO LOVE

The story of Baby Moses is one of several in the Bible where God's plan for motherhood includes adoption. Centuries after Moses was adopted by Pharoah's daughter, we read about the adoption of orphaned Esther by her cousin Mordecai. In both these instances, adoption was a natural response to a child's need for nurturing and, in Moses' case, protection.

Adoption was also a common solution for barrenness, giving a childless couple a family and the assurance that somone would look after them in old age. Sometimes, a child was adopted simply so that he would qualify for an inheritance (for example, Jacob adopted Joseph's two sons, Genesis 48:5,6).

Clearly, God recognized that the power of parenthood doesn't lie in our ability to reproduce, but in our willingness to choose both the blessings and the duties of being a mother or father.

And one more precaution—the family would give her son no name.

Of course, a baby is small, but not always quiet. How frightened the slave mother was every time her baby wailed (and how lovingly spoiled the child was as a result!). Tense weeks of trying to love and hush her baby followed. *How long can I make these stolen moments last?* the mother wondered. Would God let Pharoah snuff out the life of such a special baby?

"When will you name my little brother?" the child's older sister Miriam asked one day.

"Not until we know if…if God will let him live to need one," she said.

The day came when the mother knew her baby had gotten too big (and too loud) to hide any longer. The mother told the family she had a plan. But was it a mother's plan, or a woman's panic? Only time would tell. She decided to do what Pharoah asked—to put her child in the river. But not in quite the way the king intended.

She took a reed basket and coated it with tar and pine pitch to make a little boat. Then she wrapped her baby boy, put him in the basket, and took him down to a secluded spot on the banks of the Nile. There she hid the basket, baby and all, in the reeds.

She knew her baby might be stung by insects, might drown, or might be swallowed by a crocodile. She spilled tears while she kissed his little cheek goodbye, hoping beyond all hope that he would drift safely to another home where the threat of death to sons did not hang over the nursery.

She left Miriam with strict instructions to guard from a distance ("Don't ask so many questions—just don't take your eyes off him!" she said). The mother turned around and started for home. On that lonely walk, she poured out a flood of pleadings to heaven, *God of Abraham! God of Sarah! Save my baby boy from Pharaoh!*

Meanwhile, Miriam watched to see what would happen. And who should approach but a retinue from the palace. The enemy—so close! so soon! One of Pharaoh's own daughters had come down to the Nile to bathe.

Baby's Breath

LULL-A-BABY

Hush dear baby, hush my sweet;
The Lord is by your side
Watching o'er you as the door
To Dreamland opens wide....
Hush, hush baby, hush my sweet,
Peace be with you, Dear,
When you sleep and when you wake
The Lord is always near.

—Alice Joyce Davidson

37

These were the worst of times for boy babies. Surely, here was a baby with no future.

38

As she and her maids strolled along on the bank, the princess saw the strange floating basket. Miriam heard her command a maid to retrieve it from the waters. When she looked inside, the princess discovered a gurgling baby boy.

She guessed the terrible story right away. "He must be one of the Hebrew babies!" she said. But by now the baby was crying, and the sound melted the princess' heart. She pulled the baby to her and tried to comfort him.

Miriam, frightened but suddenly hopeful, approached the princess. Politely she asked, "Shall I go and find one of the Hebrew women to nurse the baby for you?"

"Oh, yes!" exclaimed the princess. "That's an excellent idea." So Miriam rushed home to get the best nursemaid possible—the baby's own mother.

Only hours before, all had seemed so dark. Now the mother was filled with fearful, hopeful leapings of her heart as she hurried with young Miriam back to the scene.

Calmly the princess said to the slave woman, "Take this child home and nurse him for me. I will pay you fairly." As she tenderly handed the baby to his mother, he seemed instantly comforted. The women's eyes met for just an instant—a signal that secrets could be kept, that in exchange for a mother's nurturing now, the child would be adopted into palace life later....

Many months passed, and when the child was weaned, his mother brought him back to the princess as promised. It was as hard to say good-bye this time as it had been that day by the river. But the slave mother was certain now that her child was ready for a name.

Pharaoh's daughter adopted the little Hebrew boy and named him Moses, or "draw out." As she told everyone, "I drew him out of the water. And now he's my son, prince of Egypt."

But many an evening in the years to come, the Hebrew nurse visited the palace— "to look well after the health of your foundling son," she told the princess. And to whisper stories in little Moses' ear about a mother's fierce love, a good, strong God, and a future that was certain to be his.

He Watches Over

Heavenly Father,
How great and mysterious
are your ways!

Thank you that your eye is always
on my child, And your plans
for him are great.

I cannot imagine how wonderful
you think he is.

Help me to surrender my own sweet baby
to your loving care each day, especially
when I have to entrust him
to another for a time.

Thank you that I can place him
in the dangerous river of life,
knowing that you will be watching
over him, not from far off,
but always, *always,*
right nearby.

Amen

Your plans for him are great

40

"I drew him
out of the water,
And now he's my son,
prince of Egypt."

Help from Heaven

THE BIRTH OF BABY SAMSON

See that you do not look down on one of these little ones.
For I tell you that their angels in heaven always see the face of my Father in heaven.
Matthew 8:10

Manoah always remembered the day his wife finally lost her mind. Or so it seemed. He had just sat down to dinner after a hard day planting barley, and there it was—proof enough, an absolute outpouring of silliness.

"Honey, a prophet talked to me today and maybe he was an angel he was so stunning—you have no idea, so awesome!—and he said I'll have a baby—really, a *baby!*—and a special one, too, and very important, and I'm not supposed to drink any wine and my baby will be the champion of…!" The excited woman broke for a breath.

Manoah stared. "My dear, have you been drinking?"

But his wife sat speechless, gulping air, holding her head in her hands.

Actually, Manoah wasn't too surprised. She'd been putting herself under terrible stress for years over the baby problem. Manoah knew better than anyone—and just about everyone knew—how much his wife longed to have children. But she couldn't. And now this—rantings about angels and champion babies.

After his wife calmed herself, though, things became clearer. Someone *had* visited with his wife today. An unusual man, Manoah concluded, maybe a prophet.

42

But what about the strange message? Was his dear wife to be trusted?

Manoah looked at his wife. Her eyes were still shining and sincere. Maybe she wasn't crazy.

Soon she had gathered herself and was ready to try again. "My child will be a Nazirite from birth," she declared firmly. "He will deliver us from our enemies, the Philistines—the prophet promised. We can't cut his hair. I can't eat anything unclean or drink any wine. And, of course, neither shall he."

Then she told him every detail of the story again. This time, Manoah wanted to know more. Surely, if a holy man had come to them, this baby would have no ordinary life. But without help from God, how would they ever succeed at raising a child to be both a man of God and a national hero?

Manoah wanted to see the man his wife described for himself. Just to be sure. So that evening he prayed: *"O Lord, I beg you, let the man of God you sent to us come again to teach us how to bring up the boy who is to be born"* (Judges 13:8).

Baby's Breath

BABY BY CANDLELIGHT

Beautiful baby,
gazing at me by the
light of a single white candle—
Who are you?
And who will you become?

I nurse you into the night,
until your button eyes droop
and close, and your mouth falls open,
a sweet pink oval,
a drop of milk still on your lips.

Asleep at last, your satisfied sighs—
interrupted by hiccups—
tell me all I need know about you.

Beautiful baby,
I love you.

—Heather Kopp

43

Baby in Bible Times

RAISING UP BABY FOR GOD

Manoah understood the importance of spiritual training when he asked the angel for help in raising Baby Samson. For parents in Bible times, teaching in right living began early. As soon as they could talk, Jewish children started memorizing the teachings of Moses. Paul ackowledged this when he said to Timothy, *"From infancy you have known the holy Scriptures"* (2 Timothy 3:15).

As children grew, they received instruction at the temple or synagogue. However, parents still carried the main responsibility. After Moses gave the Ten Commandments (Deuteronomy 5), he told Jewish parents, *"Impress [these commandments] on your children. Talk about them when you sit at home and when you walk along the road, when you lie down and when you get up"* (Deuteronomy 6:7). King David, writing as a young father, declared, *"Come, my children, listen to me; I will teach you the fear of the LORD"* (Psalm 34:11).

In some cases, as with Samson, a child who receives such teaching will stray. But God's child-rearing principle still holds true— *"Train a child in the way he should go, and when he is old he will not turn from it"* (Proverbs 22:6).

Several days later, it happened again. Manoah was resting in the house when he heard his wife outside yelling for him. Suddenly she flew through the door, her face flushed, her eyes big as plates. Manoah jumped up with alarm.

"He came again!" she cried. "He's here! Come quickly—please!"

Manoah hurried out. A man stood waiting for them in the newly plowed fields. He was dressed like a prophet.

"Greetings, Manoah," he said. The two men faced each other in the bright sun. Manoah wanted to shout, "Am I really to be a father? And how do you know?"

Instead he asked, "Are you the man who talked to my wife?"

"I am," the stranger said.

So Manoah started with a practical question. "When we have this child—and supposing he is set apart for God as you say—how shall we guide the boy in his life and work?"

The prophet explained again that Manoah's wife must not drink any wine or eat anything unclean. "She must do everything that I have commanded her," he explained.

"Stay for a while," Manoah said quickly. "We'll prepare a young goat for you." How could he have forgotten to be hospitable to a man sent from God?

44

But the prophet declined. "I can stay for a while, but I won't be eating. And if you wish to offer the young goat as a sacrifice instead, you should offer it to the Lord."

"When what you say comes true, we want to honor you among our friends by giving you the credit for prophesying my son's birth," Manoah said. "What is your name?"

But he only replied, "Why do you ask my name? It is beyond understanding."

Manoah was afraid to ask any more questions. While the visitor waited in the shade of an oak, Manoah set about making an offering as the man of God had suggested. He took his best young goat along with a grain offering and sacrificed it on a rock altar to the Lord. Finally, things were beginning to sink in. He and his wife had never felt so full of praise. Surely they would never see such wonders again.

But as the three stood by watching the fire consume the sacrifice, yet another wonder happened. The man of God suddenly rose in the flames and smoke, ascending in a silent rush into the glare of the sun, where he disappeared.

Surely, if a holy man had come to them, this baby would have no ordinary life.

46

"We're going to die!" cried Manoah. "We have seen God's face!" By now he realized the visitor had indeed been an angel.

This time his wife was calmer. "No," she said. "If God meant to kill us, he would not have accepted our offering, or let us see or know any of these things."

Manoah hoped his wife was right. And, as usual, she was. Not long afterward, she became pregnant and gave birth to a healthy, beautiful boy. In memory of the heavenly visitor, they named the baby Samson, meaning "sun" or "brightness."

The new mother said her baby—with his dimpled face and tiny chin—didn't look at all like a fighter, much less like one who would deliver Israel from the Philistines.

But Manoah didn't agree. "Look at his grip, honey!" he said one day, as Baby Samson clung tightly to his finger. "Why, he could pull down the gates of Gaza with those hands!"

"Maybe so," his wife murmured, "maybe so."

"...teach us how to bring up the boy who is to be born."

Help me to remember

Grant Me Wisdom

Heavenly Father,

Thank you that you promise to give
parents the wisdom and guidance they need.

Thank you for your marvelous word,
which lights the path ahead of me.

Help me to remember
that my baby does indeed have an angel
in heaven who sees your face.
How wonderful it is to know
that you have a special plan for my baby,
and that you love my baby as much
as you loved baby Samson!

May I seek you with my whole heart
as Manoah sought the advice of an angel.

And may I raise my baby to be strong
because I have sought help
from heaven.

Amen

48

Grandma's Pride and Joy

THE BIRTH OF BABY OBED

"Children's children are a crown to the aged, and parents are the pride of their children."
Proverbs 17:6

Ruth watched her mother-in-law Naomi with concern as they walked together down the last stretch of road to Bethlehem. They'd been walking for days, and the older woman was obviously exhausted and discouraged.

"We'll make friends. We'll find a good place to live…" Ruth began, trying to lift Naomi's spirits.

But what did Ruth know? Ruth had never been to Bethlehem before. She was a foreigner from Moab, Israel's enemy to the east.

As the two women trudged through the town gates, an old woman hailed them.

"Greetings, visitors! Where are you from?"

"We've come from Moab, but I'm from here—Bethlehem," Naomi said. "Many years ago…." Her voice trailed off.

"Wait," the other woman broke in. "Aren't you Naomi?"

"Yes, I am," she answered. "But don't call me Naomi anymore. Call me Mara, because God has left me bitter. I went away from here full, and, as you can see, I have come back empty."

The women walked on. Ruth knew the sorrow in her mother-in-law's heart. During Naomi's sojourn in Moab, her husband had died, then both her sons had also died. Even after 10 years of marriage, neither Ruth nor the other daughter-in-law had been able to bear children. Now Naomi was returning home widowed, childless, alone—except for her Moabite daughter-in-law.

Ruth had insisted on following her mother-in-law here. "Your people will become my people," she'd declared. "And your God will be my God."

Your people will become my people. Yes, Ruth had said that. But now as she looked around at the strange town, with people all speaking a strange language, she wondered how long it would take….

The barley harvest was just beginning in Bethlehem, and as soon as they'd gotten settled, Ruth went out to glean grain left behind by the harvesters. At the end of the first day, she came home grimy, sunburned—and smiling from ear to ear. "We're going to do just fine, Mother," she said to Naomi. "I gleaned all day, and look how much I have." She hoisted her bags of grain onto the table. "And listen, the owner of the first field I went to was so kind. He invited me to eat lunch with his workmen and to glean in his fields throughout the harvest!"

Naomi beamed. "And what is the owner's name?" she asked.

"His name is Boaz," said Ruth.

"I know Boaz!" Naomi almost shouted. "He was related to my husband. He is one of our kinsman-redeemers!" And then Naomi explained to Ruth that if a Hebrew man died without having children, his closest male relative sometimes married the man's widow so that their family name wouldn't die.

Day after day, Ruth gleaned in Boaz's fields. And night after night, she came home to tell Naomi about the harvest, and news of the town, and—of course, since Naomi always asked—Boaz.

Ruth wasn't given to girlish banter. But whenever she said something positive about Boaz, she thought she saw a gleam in Naomi's eye. Surely her mother-in-law didn't actually think a match possible? For her—a foreign girl who was probably barren?

One night Naomi said to her, "I think it's time for you to find a husband who can provide for you. You can't live on leftovers forever. And I've noticed how you feel about Boaz…"

But before Ruth could answer, Naomi plunged on. "Ruth, you must do exactly as I say." She was clasping both of Ruth's hands now. "I want you to wash and perfume yourself. Go to Boaz while he is on the threshing floor, but don't let him see you. After he's done eating and drinking, and has lain down to sleep, go to him and lie down at his feet. He will tell you what to do, according to Hebrew custom."

Often as she nursed her baby, Ruth thanked the God of Abraham, Isaac, and Naomi for her wonderful new life.

51

Baby's Breath

FAMILY TREE

In the center of life's garden
A mother gently sows
A special seed, a seed of love
That sprouts, then grows and grows.
From day to day, from year to year,
She nurtures it with care,
Yet, understanding of its needs,
She gives it room and air…
Through winter, and through summer,
Through sun and rain-filled hours,
The seedling reaches upward,
It branches, and it flowers…
In the center of life's garden
Grows a thing of majesty,
Rooted well with mother's love—
A blessed family tree!

—Alice Joyce Davidson

Ruth was startled. This seemed like a strange plan to her. But she answered, "I will do whatever you say."

The next morning Ruth could hardly wait to tell her mother-in-law how well it had gone. "Boaz wants to marry me!" Ruth announced. "He said he would be 'most honored' to redeem me, according to custom!" Now her cheeks were blushing. "But he said that another man is a closer relative to our family. By law, he has first rights to redeem. But Boaz promised to look into it. We'll just have to wait, I guess."

"Have to wait? Ha!" Naomi burst out happily. "My daughter, Boaz is following through with his promise right now! He is that kind of man, and you, my dear, are that kind of prize."

And Naomi was right. By the end of the day, Boaz was at their door. The other relative had deferred his rights. And Boaz was ready to talk about his future with Ruth.

The landowner and the gleaning girl were married as soon as harvest season was done. And by the time the new grain was sprouting in the spring, Ruth was pregnant. All her worst fears had evaporated. Later that year, Ruth presented a proud Boaz with his first child—a boy. They named him Obed.

Often as she nursed her robust, nut-brown baby, Ruth thanked the God of Abraham, Isaac, and Naomi for her wonderful new life. How much she had been blessed in so short a time!

52

Grandma Naomi, too, seemed a different person. She loved to look into Baby Obed's sweet little face and find traces of the husband she still missed, or hear Boaz's natural optimism in Obed's quick, bright laughter. "Oh, you've made my life so full again, sweetheart," Naomi would croon to her grandchild.

Naomi's friends came by to bring her congratulations and words of blessing.

Praise be to the LORD, who this day has not left you without a kinsman-redeemer. May he become famous throughout Israel! He will renew your life and sustain you in your old age. For your daughter-in-law, who loves you and who is better to you than seven sons, has given him birth (Ruth 4:14,15).

The story of Ruth and Naomi's arrival in Bethlehem and Ruth's marriage to the esteemed Boaz became a favorite baby story of their relatives. It was told and retold, especially at harvest time. But not until years later, when Ruth's great-grandson—a shepherd boy named David—was crowned king of Israel, did the family realize that their favorite baby story was even more remarkable than they'd imagined.

For now, it was joy enough for Ruth to watch Naomi with Baby Obed on her lap, whispering such secrets into the baby's ears as only a mother might—or as only a grandmother might whose heart was very, very full.

Baby in Bible Times
A BABY TO CARRY ON...

In Bible times, having babies was so important that special provisions were made for widows who were childless. The practice is described in Deuteronomy 25:5,6.

If a married man were to die without a son, one of his brothers would act as kinsman-redeemer. This meant he would marry the widow in hopes that they might have children who would carry on the family name. The kinsman was also to "redeem"—buy back—any of the deceased man's property as well, which the firstborn son would then inherit.

Originally this custom applied only to brothers. But by Ruth's time, it was extended to include any close male relative, or "next of kin." Through the kinsman-redeemer tradition, God provided a second chance for childless women to become mothers and—much to Naomi's delight— for parents to become grandparents.

53

54

a part of us lives on

From Generation to Generation

Heavenly Father,

How easy it is to forget that this baby
is not just a gift to me, but to all
my relatives as well!

You planned it this way,
that each baby would be a sign of joy,
a source of pride, a new green shoot
sprouting up in our family tree.

And in this way, a part of us lives on.

Oh, it is too wonderful for words
to know that my baby may someday have
a baby, and that baby, a baby…

I pray that you would help me to be as
generous with my baby as Ruth was with hers.

May I always remember that this baby
does not belong only to me,
but first to you, and also
to my whole family.

Amen

"Oh, you've made my life so full again, sweetheart..."

A Mother's Gift

Sons are a heritage from the LORD, children a reward from him.

Psalm 127:3

Year after year, it was the same. No, Hannah decided, it was worse! Either Peninnah's cruel jabs were growing sharper, or Hannah was taking Peninnah's insults more to heart.

Peninnah was the other wife of Hannah's husband, Elkanah. She was the wife who had born Elkanah heirs— and would never let Hannah forget it.

Now Elkanah's family and friends were on their yearly journey to Shiloh for the festival of thanks. They walked through grain fields and pastures lush with new life.

"Oh, it's so hard to keep track of all my babies!" Peninnah called out in mock frustration to a friend. Then she leaned close to whisper in another woman's ear. They shook their heads and glanced in Hannah's direction.

Hannah knew their thoughts. Her womb was like a rocky hillside, not one of these fertile fields. No seed would take root in her. For Hannah, these journeys to celebrate God's goodness had turned into pilgrimages of pain.

As they walked along toward

56

Shiloh, Hannah's thoughts turned to wondering what terrible sin she had committed to make God forsake her so.

Elkanah knew that Peninnah tormented Hannah, but he had no idea how frequently or how cruelly. Often, Peninnah made her so upset on these trips that Hannah couldn't even eat.

Privately, Elkanah tried to encourage Hannah. Peninnah, he said, could give him children. But Hannah gave him a partner, a wife, a lover.

When the family reached Shiloh, and it was time to make the sacrifice, Elkanah gave Peninnah and her children each one portion of meat, but he gave Hannah two. He always did. "Because I love you," he would whisper.

That night, her husband found Hannah crying again. *"Hannah why are you weeping?"* he said. *"Why don't you eat? Why are you down-hearted? Don't I mean more to you than ten sons?"* (1 Samuel 1:8).

Whenever Elkanah asked her such questions, Hannah couldn't answer. How could a man ever understand the aching need to be a mother? Yes, she was glad for Elkanah's love, and that he hadn't divorced her for her barrenness. But he couldn't take the place of a baby.

That day, Hannah was in great anguish. She wondered about Elkanah's ritual of giving her two portions. Was it more than a sweet gesture? Couldn't it also be a gift of faith?

Suddenly she knew what she must do. Standing in the temple courtyard, she raised her hands and began to pray from the depths of her being. Others looked on in bewilderment at her public display.

"May God grant you what you ask of him."

57

Baby's Breath

THE BEAUTIFUL

Three things there are more beautiful
Than any man could wish to see:
The first, it is a full-rigged ship
Sailing with all her sails set free;
The second, when the wind and sun
Are playing in a field of corn;
The third, a woman, young and fair,
Showing her child before it is born.

—W. H. Davies

58

But Hannah knew that this was the time and place for her to make God a promise.

"O Lord Almighty," she prayed, *"if you will only look upon your servant's misery and remember me, and not forget your servant but give her a son, then I will give him to the Lord for all the days of his life, and no razor will ever be used on his head"* (1 Samuel 1:11).

As Hannah made her radical vow—gently swaying, lips moving, tears streaming down—Eli the priest was watching. He scurried over. "What are you doing here drunk, woman? Get rid of your wine!" he scolded.

Hannah was stunned. "Oh, no!" she cried. "I haven't been drinking, only praying to the Lord. I am in great anguish. Please don't think I am a wicked woman!"

Eli saw immediately that she told the truth. "Go in peace, my daughter," he said gently. "And may God grant you what you have asked of him."

May he! May he! pleaded Hannah, as she gathered her skirts and sat down. She wiped away her tears. By the time she left the courtyard, her spirits had lifted. *He may! He may!* she said over and over in her heart.

When the family had returned home to Ramah, Hannah told Elkanah about her vow and about Eli's blessing. "Elkanah dear, if you have faith now, take me in your arms," she said. She was smiling.

Every night that she slept with her husband, Hannah hoped. And each time, it hurt her to hope. But not as much as having no hope at all.

Soon, Hannah could dismiss the changes in her body no longer. *Pregnant!* She could hardly believe it. Every morning, she ran her hands over her tummy, waiting to feel it grow. And each day as the pregnancy progressed, she noticed that Peninnah's taunts faded.

Elkanah loved the way his dear Hannah glowed, and when she gave birth to a son, he glowed too. Hannah named her baby Samuel, which means "Heard of God." "Because I asked the Lord for him," she said.

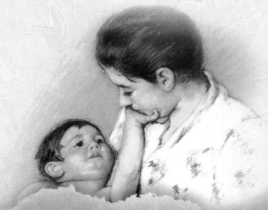

Baby in Bible Times
BRINGING BABY TO JESUS

Few parents have to make the kind of drastic surrender that Hannah made when she brought young Samuel to live at the temple. But when modern parents take their baby forward at church for christening or dedication, they're following an ancient impulse to acknowledge that Baby really belongs to Father God.

Hebrew parents had a keen sense that their children were gifts of God—and ultimately belonged to him. Firstborn sons were "bought back" from the priests for five pieces of silver—a powerful reminder of how God had saved Jewish firstborn sons from death during the plagues of Egypt.

When we dedicate Baby to God, we are giving the child back to God in gratitude and worship. But we are also asking for God to touch our child in a special way for the years ahead. A favorite passage in the New Testament shows parents bringing their babies to Jesus for his blessing. When the disciples tried to intervene (so the Lord could give his time to more "important" matters), Jesus says, *"Let the little children come to me, and do not hinder them, for the kingdom of God belongs to such as these"* (Luke 18: 16,17).

59

When the day came to take Samuel to the temple, Hannah felt gratitude, and peace—and a little shaky.

60

Watching Samuel kick and cry, Hannah thanked God for his remarkable gift of babies and motherhood—and prayed that God would help her to keep her promise.

The next year when festival time came around, Hannah told her husband with a twinkle, "Save me two portions!" But she stayed home with her newborn. The years that followed filled her mother's heart with happiness. As little Samuel nursed, she gazed at his small, puckering mouth and bright, brown eyes, and wondered what great plan God might have for her baby.

When the day came to take Samuel to the temple, Hannah felt gratitude, and peace—and a little shaky. Together, she and Elkanah sought out Eli. "Here is the baby I prayed for right in front of you," explained Hannah. "I vowed to give him to God. And now, here he is. He is ready to serve the Lord for the rest of his life."

And then she broke out in a song:
My heart rejoices in the LORD;
in the LORD my horn is lifted high.
My mouth boasts over my enemies,
for I delight in your deliverance.
There is no one holy like the LORD;
there is no one besides you; there is
no Rock like our God…
(1Samuel 2:1,2).

Then Hannah and Elkanah left Samuel with Eli and went home to Ramah. Every day, Hannah's heart and prayers were with her son. She visited him often, and every year brought him a new coat just for the festival of thanks.

At every visit, Eli would bless Elkanah and his wife with the same prayer: *May the LORD give you children by this woman to take the place of the one she gave to the LORD* (1 Samuel 1:20).

The Lord answered that prayer, too. In fact, at the festival not many years later, Elkanah had to give Hannah *five* portions for her lively brood of daughters and other sons!

And much to Hannah's delight—but not at all to her surprise—Samuel, the son she gave back to God, grew up to be one of Israel's greatest prophets.

61

Grant me the courage

My Baby Is Yours

Heavenly Father,

How I thank you for the gift
of my baby. Each baby that is born
to a mother is indeed a gift
of great worth. And yet, it is also a gift
you ask us to give back to you.

Help me to remember that although
I am a mother, my baby doesn't belong
only to me, but also to you, Lord.

Grant me the courage of Hannah to hand my
baby back over to your loving care.

For you, Heavenly Father, know
what is best for my baby's whole life.

May you have your hand on
my baby all of his days!

Amen

"Go in peace, my daughter..."

In the Secret Place

My frame was not hidden from you when I was made in the secret place.
When I was woven together in the depths of the earth, your eyes saw my unformed body.
All the days ordained for me were written in your book before one of them came to be.
Psalm 139:15,16

Elizabeth and Zechariah often said that they had spent their whole life waiting. The prophets had promised a Messiah for troubled Israel. And promised. But when would he appear in God's temple to deliver his suffering people?

Every day Elizabeth watched Zechariah leave for his duties at the temple—cleaning, caring for the scrolls, helping worshipers prepare their hearts to worship God.

"Maybe today," he would say to Elizabeth at the door.

When they were younger, they had waited for a baby, too. But Elizabeth's season for motherhood had come and gone. They had chosen instead to give their lives waiting for another baby—the child promised to bring salvation.

One day the waiting stopped. When Elizabeth met her husband at the door that evening, he greeted her with strange gestures and even stranger silence—he was unable to speak. Elizabeth feared the worst. Had her Zechariah been struck with the first blight of old age? Was this the beginning of the end?

64

But when she finally found a tablet for him to write on, her husband scribbled down an amazing story. "An angel came to me," he wrote. "The angel's name was Gabriel. He said that you would have a baby that we are to name John! He will prepare the way before the Lord."

The couple looked at each other, stunned. "So why can't you speak?" she pleaded.

Zechariah continued scribbling. "When I questioned the angel about this being possible, since you…since we are getting older, the angel took my voice away."

Elizabeth flung her arms around her husband. He was a good man. He wouldn't lie. An angel? A baby? Yes, *a baby!* Elizabeth's whole being began to tremble. Something astounding was unfolding.

Only weeks later, Elizabeth knew. She was pregnant. As the days passed, her face took on the glow of young motherhood and her tummy grew. *"The Lord has done this for me,"* she said. *"In these days he has shown his favor and taken away my disgrace among the people"* (Luke 1:25).

Elizabeth stayed in near-seclusion for five months. Her pregnancy, her husband's affliction, the angel…it was all too complicated to try to explain. Meanwhile, Zechariah continued to fulfill his duties at the temple, although he was still unable to speak. But his face…his face spoke to Elizabeth every day of fatherly pride and anticipation.

Baby in Bible Times
WORLD, HERE I COME!

When Elizabeth's second-trimester baby jumped in her womb, it was confirmation to both Elizabeth and Mary that Mary was indeed carrying the Christ. Readers today find another powerful confirmation: that a baby while yet in the womb is a human being capable of responding to God.

The Bible tells other baby stories where God identifies a child, describes his destiny, and gives him a name before or during gestation (for example, the pregnancies of Sarah, Rebecca, and Samson's mother).

Imagine how astonished parents in ancient times would be about modern debates over when human life begins. David summed up the biblical perspective simply and eloquently when he wrote, *"You brought me out of the womb; you made me trust in you even at my mother's breast….from my mother's womb you have been my God"* (Psalm 22:9,10).

65

Zechariah's face...his face spoke to Elizabeth every day of fatherly pride and anticipation.

66

One day, while Elizabeth was in her sixth month, she had a visitor. When she went to the door, she heard her cousin Mary calling out a greeting. At that instant, the child in her womb gave a tremendous leap. Then Elizabeth herself was overcome with the Holy Spirit.

She held up both hands toward her young cousin, and before she knew what she was saying, she exclaimed to Mary,

Blessed are you among women, and blessed is the child you will bear! But why am I so favored, that the mother of my LORD should come to me?…Blessed is she who has believed that what the LORD has said to her will be accomplished! (Luke 1:42-45).

Mary, who was also expecting, was thrilled by Elizabeth's prophetic blessing. "And I see my dear cousin has been been visited by blessing as well," she said with a voice full of laughter. And then the two sat down to tell and retell every detail of their marvelous stories.

Mary stayed with Elizabeth for three wonderful months. At night, Zechariah listened to the women talk about the future. Sometimes he would scratch out a hurried note or two and hand it to them. And sometimes what he gave them were carefully copied passages from the scroll of Isaiah. God's promises, he reminded them.

But all three agreed that the wonder of God's plan was described in one bouncing, beautiful word—*Baby!*

Soon after Mary left, Elizabeth's time for delivery arrived, and she had a son. Neighbors came by to ooh and ahh over her sleeping child. "It's a miracle!" they all agreed.

On the eighth day, the baby was ready for the traditional ceremony of circumcision and naming. Friends assumed that the child might be named after his father to memorialize such a remarkable event, but when an uncle held up a cooing "little Zechariah" for presentation, Elizabeth spoke up.

"No! His name is John," she said firmly.

"But," they objected, "there's no one in your family with that name."

All eyes went to Zechariah. He asked for a writing tablet and, to everyone's astonishment, wrote out in bold letters, "John." At that very moment, his voice returned. And soon the clamor of the family celebration was joined by another sound—the voice of Zechariah praising God.

Elizabeth watched, amazed, as words of prophecy and blessing tumbled now from her husband:

Baby's Breath
WHERE DID YOU COME FROM, BABY DEAR?

Where did you come from, baby dear?
Out of everywhere into here…
Where did you get that little tear?
I found it waiting when I got here.
—George MacDonald

67

All agreed that the wonder of God's plan was described in one bouncing, beautiful word — Baby!

68

…And you, my child, will be called a prophet of the Most High; for you will go on before the Lord to prepare the way for him, to give his people the knowledge of salvation through the forgiveness of their sins, because of the tender mercy of our God, by which the rising sun will come to us from heaven to shine on those living in darkness and in the shadow of death, to guide our feet into the path of peace (Luke 1:76-79).

For many years to come, people traded stories about that day, and about Zechariah's words. Would the son of Elizabeth and Zechariah grow up to be another Elijah? How long would they have to wait to know?

But Elizabeth wasn't wondering or waiting. From the day Zechariah had been struck silent, she knew a miracle had been forming deep inside her. And from the moment her unborn son had leaped for joy in Mary's presence, Elizabeth was certain that Baby John had already begun to carry out his important destiny.

...*Elizabeth knew* a miracle had been forming deep inside her.

My Heart Leaps for Joy

Heavenly Father,

You are the Maker of all that is good
and innocent and worthy of praise.
How I thank you for the baby you have given
me. I rejoice in her destiny, and the part I get to
play in helping her to grow up to fulfill it.
I am so amazed at how far you plan ahead!
And yet, it is so good to know that you
have a plan for all babies, while they are yet in
their mother's womb!
No baby is hidden from you there
nor do you wait to breathe your Spirit of Life
upon such small ones until they
are delivered to us, crying, gasping—
and beautiful!
For this I praise and thank you.
My heart, and perhaps my baby's, leap for joy
because you are near.

Amen

For this I praise you

70

God's Own Baby

For God so loved the world that he gave his one and only Son,
that whoever believes in him shall not perish but have eternal life.

John 3:16

Mary had grown up hearing stories about angels visiting women. Some of the stories were famous. Everyone knew about Hannah, Sarah, and Samson's mother.

But the last thing on her mind tonight was angels. Or even babies. These days she was thinking of Joseph day and night. She was pledged to be married to him, and unlike some of her friends who didn't care for the young man their parents betrothed them to, Mary thought she would come to love Joseph.

Or, at least, she thought she would from what she'd seen of him so far. Joseph had honest eyes. And what must be the strongest hands in Nazareth.

Tonight Mary was lying on her bed trying to conjure up in her mind Joseph's exact face. Brown skin, wiry, black hair…

She gasped and sat up. Right in front of her stood a man— no, an angel!

"Greetings, you who are highly favored! The Lord is with you!" the angel said.

What did he mean? "I am just Mary!" she wanted to cry. "You're mistaken!" But she was too afraid to speak.

Then the angel said kindly,

Do not be afraid, Mary, you have found favor with God. You will be with child and give birth to a son, and you are to give him the name Jesus.

71

"*Mary,*" *Joseph whispered in an urgent voice.* "*I know that you are with child. And I know why...*"

72

He will be great and will be called the Son of the Most High. The Lord God will give him the throne of his father David, and he will reign over the house of Jacob forever; his kingdom will never end (Luke 1:30-33).

Mary could hardly believe the angel's presence, much less his words. And what he had just said was too much to take in so quickly. Not to mention impossible! When she finally found her voice, she asked softly, "How…can this be, since… I am a virgin?" To discuss such things, even with an angel, was embarrassing.

The angel understood her question.

The Holy Spirit will come upon you, and the power of the Most High will overshadow you. So the holy one to be born will be called the Son of God. Even Elizabeth your relative is going to have a child in her old age, and she who was said to be barren is in her sixth month. For nothing is impossible with God (Luke 1:35-37).

Nothing is impossible? Mary believed with her whole heart that this was true. And if God had a special task for her, she wanted to fulfill it. Her heart pounded. "I am the Lord's servant," she said. "May it be to me as you have said."

And then the angel was gone.

Mary sat trembling. An hour passed. As the vision of the angel began to fade, Mary made a decision. She would go straight to Elizabeth's house. She lived three-days' journey away. Mary could find some privacy there, and someone to talk to…

But from the moment she arrived on Elizabeth's doorstep, more surprises unfolded. For a greeting, Elizabeth burst out with a prophecy from the Holy Spirit: *"Blessed are you among women, and blessed is the child you will bear! But why am I so favored, that the mother of my Lord should come to me?"* (Luke 1:42).

Her cousin's words filled Mary with reassurance. She had not been dreaming or ill!

No sooner had the two embraced, when Elizabeth poured out her own story of a visit from the angel Gabriel, the child in her own womb, and Zechariah's mysterious speechlessness.

For three joyous months, the two women cooked together, took walks in the hills, and tried to grasp the miracle that God was performing.

But then it was time to return home. All the way, Mary could not escape one nagging fear: What about Joseph? Even Elizabeth hadn't been much help here. How does a woman who is still a virgin explain to her betrothed husband, especially one as upright and practical as Joseph, that she is going to have a baby whose father is God?

Baby's Breath
HUSH! MY DEAR

Hush, my dear! Lie still and slumber;
Holy angels guard thy bed!
Heavenly blessings without number
Gently falling on thy head.

How much better thou'rt attended
Than the Son of God could be,
When from heaven He descended
And became a child like thee!

Mayest thou live to know and fear Him
Trust and love Him all thy days;
Then go dwell forever near Him
See His face, and sing His praise.

—Isaac Watts

73

Her sleeping child was God's own baby, the Savior that the world had been waiting so long to see.

74

As Mary approached Nazareth, she saw a man coming toward her on the dusty road. Then she realized with alarm that it was Joseph. What was she going to say?

But Joseph had much to say to her instead. "Mary," he whispered in an urgent voice. "I know that you are with child. And I know why…"

Mary met his eyes, amazed. "How could you…?"

Joseph motioned that he wanted to continue. "An angel came to me, Mary!" he said. "In a dream. And he told me not to divorce you. You see, I heard the rumor that you were with child, Mary. The angel told me to marry you, that you were carrying God's child. His name is Jesus, Messiah…"

Mary had never heard Joseph say so much at once. His news was too wonderful to grasp. She began to pour out her own story to him, including the angel's visit to Elizabeth. After she was done, the two were quiet for some time. This miracle of God in Mary's womb seemed so far beyond words.

Soon a simple wedding took place, and Joseph took Mary as his wife. He lay near her in the dark night after night, but he never asked her to consummate their marriage in lovemaking.

All during the months of her growing pregnancy, she and Joseph prayed and waited and wondered. Would this baby, conceived by God and without a man, look or behave differently from other babies? Would he ever really be theirs? And why would God choose two such ordinary people to bring his Son into the world?

Toward the end of Mary's pregnancy, startling news arrived. By government decree, the two would have to return to Joseph's hometown, Bethlehem, to register for a national census. There was nothing to be done but go. During the entire hot, jarring trip, Mary felt that the baby might come any minute.

When they arrived in Bethlehem, the town was so crowded because of the census that they couldn't find a place to stay. While Joseph was being turned away at the last inn on his list, Mary's labor pains came upon her. When the innkeeper heard her cry and saw what was happening, he said, "You two might be wise to make use of my stable tonight. At least it's newly cleaned."

Baby in Bible Times
A MOTHER'S SACRIFICE OF PRAISE

During Bible times, a woman who had just given birth was considered "unpure," or "unclean." She was required not to leave her home for seven days and was not allowed to particpate in religous ceremonies for another 33 days. At the end of this time she was to make both a burnt offering and a sin offering. "Then she will be ceremonially clean from her flow of blood" (Leviticus 12:7).

A year-old lamb was preferred for the burnt offering, but a poor woman was allowed to sacrifice birds for both offerings. We read in Luke's account that Mary sacrificed two turtle doves after the birth of Jesus.

Today, because of Jesus' once-for-all sacrifice on the cross, a mother doesn't have to present special offerings to regain purity. Instead, all our gifts to God can be sacrifices of praise, thanks, and worship. We can sing with Mary, *"The Mighty One has done great things for me—holy is his name"* (Luke 1:49).

75

Joseph quickly said yes, and the two moved their travel bundles into an empty stall. Night fell. The sounds of the city quieted. And Mary's contractions began in earnest.

"Aren't we sinning to let the Son of God be born in a cattle stall?" Mary asked Joseph. "This is so…unsuitable!"

"I am sorry, Mary," Joseph said. "I don't understand either…"

Then the innkeeper's wife entered to help with the delivery. Just as she was shooing Joseph out, Mary was swept into another contraction. And not many minutes later, amid the smells of cattle and sheep and the rustling of straw, Mary gave birth.

They named the baby Jesus, as the angel had said, and made a bed for him in a manger.

Just before dawn, they were wakened by a band of young shepherds rapping hesitantly at the gate. "What do you want?" Joseph asked. "We've just had a birth here and…"

"Yes! We know!" the shepherds exclaimed, almost in unison. "Angels told us a savior was born tonight! Right here!" They said an angel had even told them exactly where to find the baby. "He is Christ the Lord!" they declared.

When Joseph let the excited men into the stable, they fell on their faces in the straw and worshiped the tiny sleeping form.

Mary knew that what the shepherds said was true. Her sleeping child was God's own baby, the Savior that the world had been waiting so long to see. But as she held up her baby for the shepherds to admire, his fresh, damp skin smelled to her like any newborn's. And his wonderful little sighs played in her heart like the sounds of a harp.

She couldn't voice such thoughts or put all her feelings to words. But she stored them in her soul like treasures. And she held her baby close.

Would this baby look or behave differently from other babies?

77

Thank You for Your Son

Heavenly Father,

You sent your baby to save my baby.

You sent your own perfect Son into this
broken world, in order to save
and heal the world.

And now, I pray that my baby would grow
up to know and love your Son, Jesus,
and become part of your eternal family.

May my baby recognize you anywhere—
in a grand palace, in a manger,
at school, or at home—
and respond with worship and joy.

Thank you for allowing me to become
a mother, along with Eve, Mary,
and so many mothers in between
and since then!

Amen

May my baby recognize you

Her sleeping child
was God's own baby...